place your photo here

an
ADVENTURE
in every
like

a gift for:

____

from:

____

year:

____

message:

____

instructions

1. open the i like book
2. place pen in hand
3. write something you like about your child today
4. smile ☺ you just made someone feel special because you noticed something unique about them
5. repeat process the next day, and keep looking for those likes

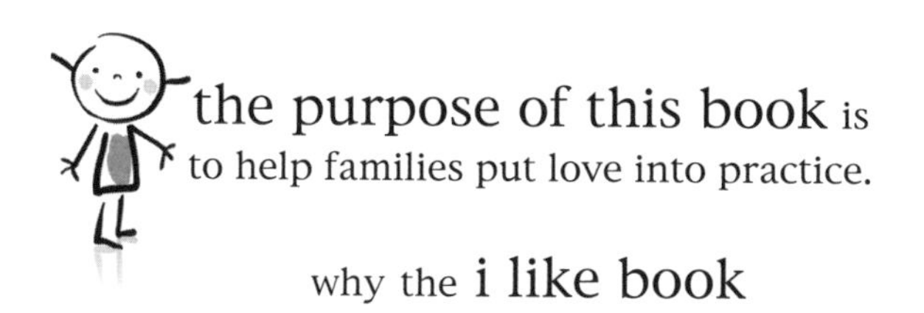

the purpose of this book is to help families put love into practice.

why the i like book

do your children know what you like about them? have you ever thought about what you really like about your children? the i like book reserves a moment each day that is focused only on your children. They will grow to crave this positive attention while you, the parent, start to see the endless things you like in them.

how to use the i like book

write a short i like statement daily in your children's i like book, something you like about them, and share it with your children. try incorporating this activity into your bedtime routine. the like can be affectionate, funny, loving, silly, warm, complimentary, or anything special.

history of the i like book

when we were first married, we started leaving i like notes for one another. eventually, there were so many, it was difficult to keep track of them. we bought a notebook and began this routine daily. soon, our two sons joined our family, and each received a book. starting a new book each year in a regular notebook became challenging and frustrating. we felt compelled to create the i like book so that we might share the i like experience with others. this book is in a twelve-month layout sequence which makes it easy and fun to use. when filled with all of your i likes, it will be a cherished gift forever!

"kind words are short and easy to speak but their echoes are truly endless"

—mother theresa

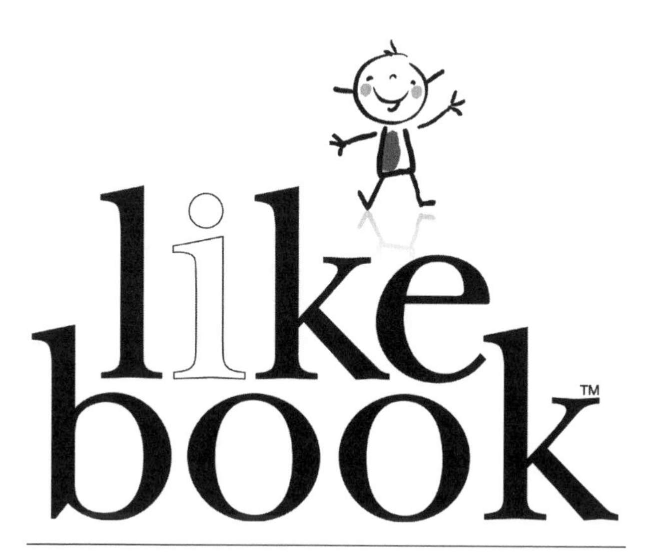

touching hearts one like at a time

created by

meredith & lance j. looney

design & layout by

jani duncan smith, it girl design, llc

our guarantee:

we believe so strongly in the message of the i like book that we are making this quality guarantee to you. if for any reason you are disappointed with the i like book's ability to make a difference with your children, we will refund the purchase price of the book. to help us serve you better please send in the order form page and briefly describe the situation.

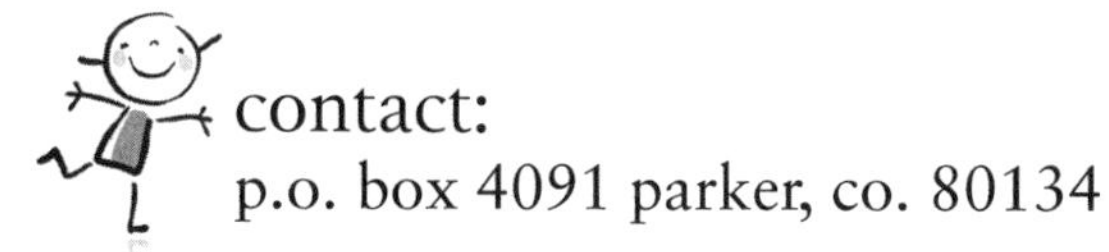

contact:

p.o. box 4091 parker, co. 80134

special discounts:

for information on wholesale pricing please contact us at 888.737.like (5453) or visit our website www.theilikebook.com

printed in the usa. i like books are eco-friendly, made with 30% post-consumer recycled fiber, soy based ink and acid free paper.

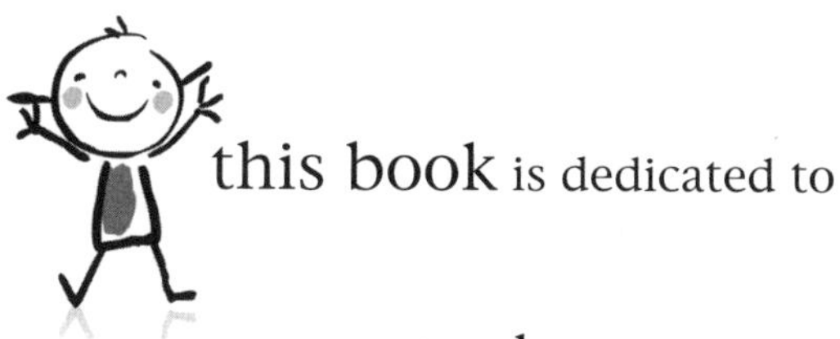

this book is dedicated to

our boys

jackson:

Mom I Like ... how you are both sweet & tough all wrapped into one.

Dad I Like ... watching you live your life as adventurously as you do.

austin:

Mom I Like ... your big bear hugs and butterfly kisses.

Dad I Like ... how your sense of humor lights up our house.

(this is also an example of what your entries might look like)

thank you for taking the like journey with us. we are so excited for you to experience the joy and magic of the i like book with your children. the i like book was created to nurture and inspire each child's human spirit. our wish and guarantee is that the i like book brings peace and happiness into your home in the most natural way possible. the i like book is immediately impactful and forever cherished!

enjoy,

Meredith & Lance

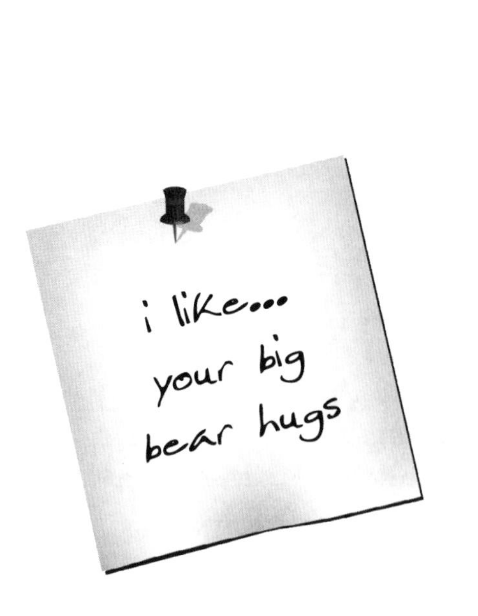

i like...
when you
say funny
things

i like...
holding
your hand

i like...
how sweet
you are

Jan 2014
month

day 1:
Mom
written by
parent, grandparent, etc.
i like ... your giggles.

written by
parent, grandparent, etc.
i like ...

day 2:
Dad
i like ... when you read books

i like ...

day 3:
Mom
i like ... When you give me hugs and kisses

Pop pop Lenny
i like ... when you take me by the hand to the potty & talk about my chicken neck

day ~~4~~ 3:
GiGi
i like ... your loud farts & protects his sister

i like ...

day 5:
dad
i like ... when you use your imagination

i like ... when you make Eliza laugh

day 6:
i like ...

i like ...

day 7:
i like ...

i like ...

i like...spending time with you.

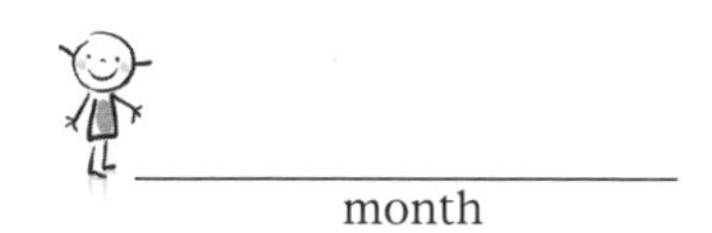

month

day 8:

written by parent, grandparent, etc. i like ...

written by parent, grandparent, etc. i like ...

day 9:

i like ...

i like ...

day 10:

i like ...

i like ...

day 11:

i like ...

i like ...

day 12:

i like ...

i like ...

day 13:

i like ...

i like ...

day 14:

i like ...

i like ...

i like...spending time with you.

sketch page

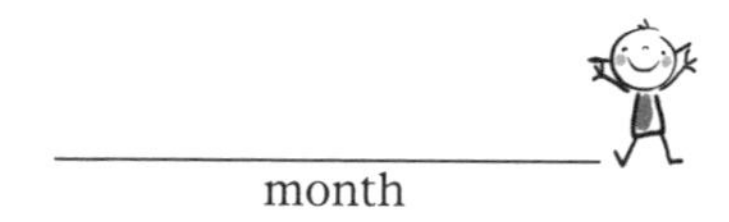

day 15:

written by
parent, grandparent, etc. i like ...

written by
parent, grandparent, etc. i like ...

day 16:

i like ...

i like ...

day 17:

i like ...

i like ...

day 18:

i like ...

i like ...

day 19:

i like ...

i like ...

day 20:

i like ...

i like ...

day 21:

i like ...

i like ...

i like...spending time with you.

how are you feeling today?

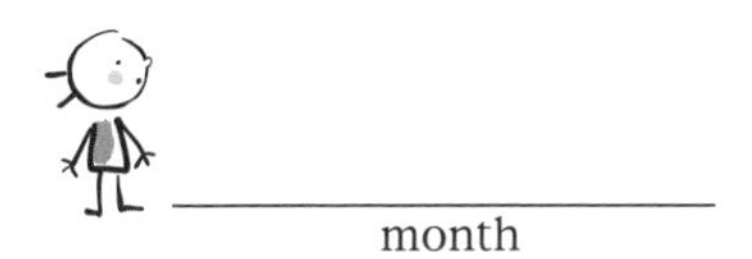

month

day 22:

written by
parent, grandparent, etc. i like ...

written by
parent, grandparent, etc. i like ...

day 23:

i like ...

i like ...

day 24:

i like ...

i like ...

day 25:

i like ...

i like ...

day 26:

i like ...

i like ...

day 27:

i like ...

i like ...

day 28:

i like ...

i like ...

i like...spending time with you.

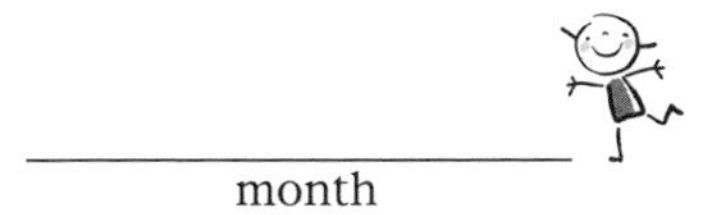

month

day 29:

written by parent, grandparent, etc. i like ...

written by parent, grandparent, etc. i like ...

day 30:

i like ...

i like ...

day 31:

i like ...

i like ...

just for kids

what do you like about your family, friends, life or you?

my name i like ...

i like ...

i like ...

(kids too young to write? feel free to write on their behalf.)

BEDTIME

is **NOT** *only for*

SAYING GOODNIGHT

it's for saying what
i like about you

________________ 
month

day 1:

______ written by ______ i like ... ________________

____

______ written by ______ i like ... ________________

____

day 2:

________________ i like ... ________________

____

________________ i like ... ________________

____

day 3:

________________ i like ... ________________

____

________________ i like ... ________________

____

day 4:

________________ i like ... ________________

____

________________ i like ... ________________

____

day 5:

________________ i like ... ________________

____

________________ i like ... ________________

____

day 6:

________________ i like ... ________________

____

________________ i like ... ________________

____

day 7:

________________ i like ... ________________

____

________________ i like ... ________________

____

i like...watching you play.

"kids spell love **time**."

—john crudele

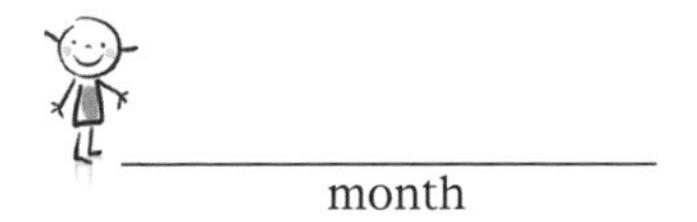

month

day 8:

written by i like ...

written by i like ...

day 9:

i like ...

i like ...

day 10:

i like ...

i like ...

day 11:

i like ...

i like ...

day 12:

i like ...

i like ...

day 13:

i like ...

i like ...

day 14:

i like ...

i like ...

i like...watching you play.

"if you sleep in your clothes you won't have to get dressed in the morning"

—stephanie

place your photo here

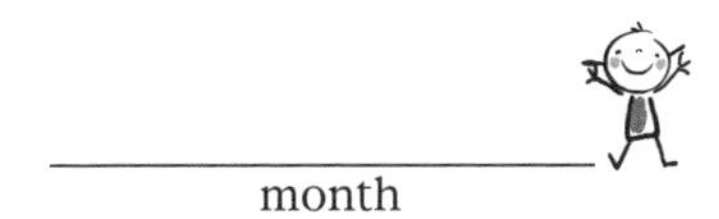

month

day 15:

written by ________ i like ... ________

____

written by ________ i like ... ________

____

day 16:

________ i like ... ________

____

________ i like ... ________

____

day 17:

________ i like ... ________

____

________ i like ... ________

____

day 18:

________ i like ... ________

____

________ i like ... ________

____

day 19:

________ i like ... ________

____

________ i like ... ________

____

day 20:

________ i like ... ________

____

________ i like ... ________

____

day 21:

________ i like ... ________

____

________ i like ... ________

____

i like...watching you play.

design it ...

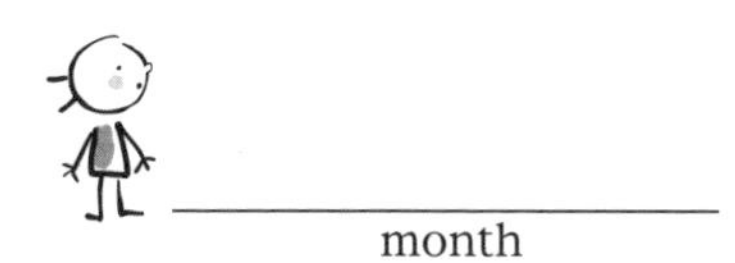

month

day 22:

written by ______ i like ... ______

written by ______ i like ... ______

day 23:

______ i like ... ______

______ i like ... ______

day 24:

______ i like ... ______

______ i like ... ______

day 25:

______ i like ... ______

______ i like ... ______

day 26:

______ i like ... ______

______ i like ... ______

day 27:

______ i like ... ______

______ i like ... ______

day 28:

______ i like ... ______

______ i like ... ______

i like...watching you play.

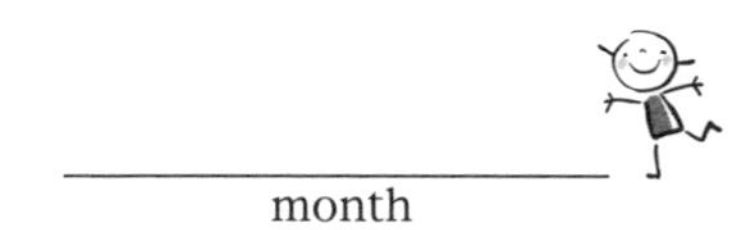

month

day 29:

written by ______ i like ... ______

written by ______ i like ... ______

day 30:

______ i like ... ______

______ i like ... ______

day 31:

______ i like ... ______

______ i like ... ______

just for kids

what do you like about your family, friends, life or you?

my name ______ i like ... ______

______ i like ... ______

______ i like ... ______

(kids too young to write? feel free to write on their behalf.)

you make me smile all over my face ~ian
i like
you

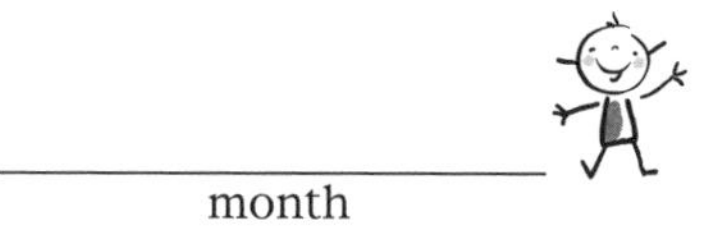

month

day 1:

written by i like ...

written by i like ...

day 2:

i like ...

i like ...

day 3:

i like ...

i like ...

day 4:

i like ...

i like ...

day 5:

i like ...

i like ...

day 6:

i like ...

i like ...

day 7:

i like ...

i like ...

i like...your smile.

as they grow ...

10,905
number of
diapers changed
0-3 years

357
number of
"why" questions
asked daily
4-5 years

6-8
years old
kids double their
speaking and
listening vocabularies

623
slices of
pizza eaten
9-11 years

1,500
average number of text
messages exchanged
per month
12-14 years

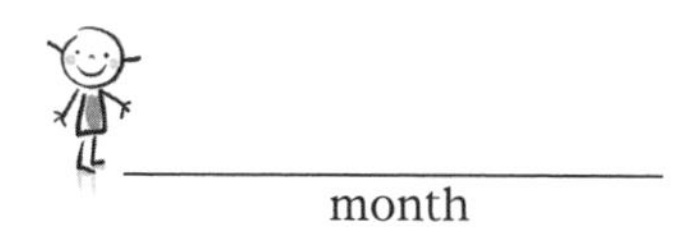

day 8:

written by ______ i like ... ______

written by ______ i like ... ______

day 9:

______ i like ... ______

______ i like ... ______

day 10:

______ i like ... ______

______ i like ... ______

day 11:

______ i like ... ______

______ i like ... ______

day 12:

______ i like ... ______

______ i like ... ______

day 13:

______ i like ... ______

______ i like ... ______

day 14:

______ i like ... ______

______ i like ... ______

squiggle

month

day 15:

written by ____ i like ... ____

written by ____ i like ... ____

day 16:

____ i like ... ____

____ i like ... ____

day 17:

____ i like ... ____

____ i like ... ____

day 18:

____ i like ... ____

____ i like ... ____

day 19:

____ i like ... ____

____ i like ... ____

day 20:

____ i like ... ____

____ i like ... ____

day 21:

____ i like ... ____

____ i like ... ____

i like...your smile.

tic tac toe

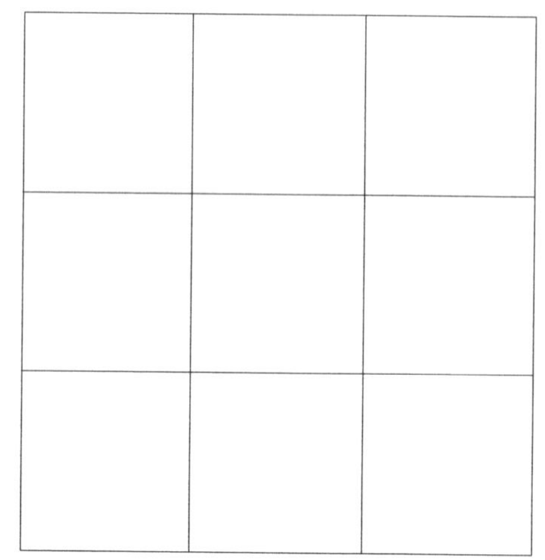

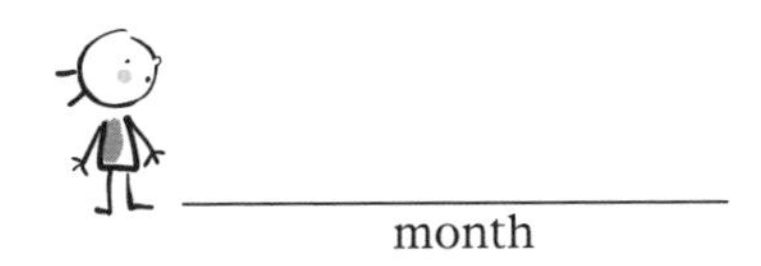

day 22:

written by i like ...

written by i like ...

day 23:

i like ...

i like ...

day 24:

i like ...

i like ...

day 25:

i like ...

i like ...

day 26:

i like ...

i like ...

day 27:

i like ...

i like ...

day 28:

i like ...

i like ...

i like...your smile.

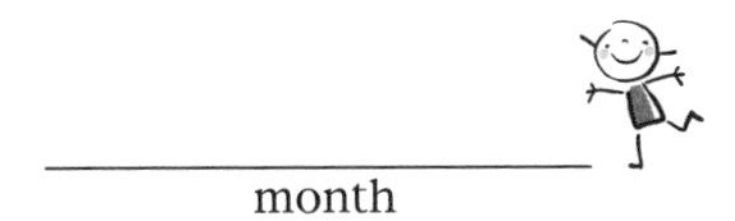

day 29:

written by ____________ i like ... ____________

written by ____________ i like ... ____________

day 30:

____________ i like ... ____________

____________ i like ... ____________

day 31:

____________ i like ... ____________

____________ i like ... ____________

just for kids

what do you like about your family, friends, life or you?

my name ____________ i like ... ____________

____________ i like ... ____________

____________ i like ... ____________

(kids too young to write? feel free to write on their behalf.)

l *live*

i *in*

k *kindness*

e *everyday*

month

day 1:

written by i like ...

written by i like ...

day 2:

i like ...

i like ...

day 3:

i like ...

i like ...

day 4:

i like ...

i like ...

day 5:

i like ...

i like ...

day 6:

i like ...

i like ...

day 7:

i like ...

i like ...

today i am ...

AGE

HEIGHT
WEIGHT

GRADE

I LIVE IN

HAPPIEST WHEN

FAVORITE COLOR

FAVORITE THING TO DO

FAVORITE FOOD

MY FRIENDS ARE

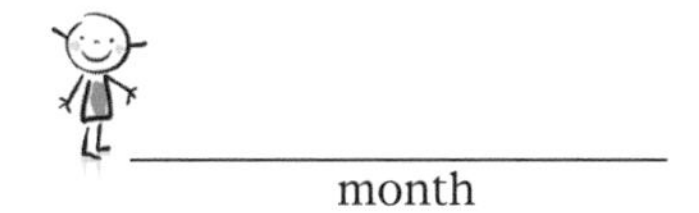

month

day 8:

written by i like ...

written by i like ...

day 9:

i like ...

i like ...

day 10:

i like ...

i like ...

day 11:

i like ...

i like ...

day 12:

i like ...

i like ...

day 13:

i like ...

i like ...

day 14:

i like ...

i like ...

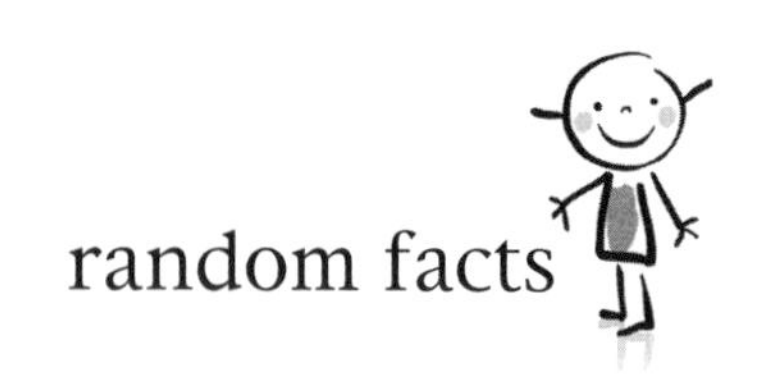

random facts

7,000 new insect species are discovered every year

a cow gives nearly 200,000 glasses of milk in her lifetime

a hippo can open its mouth wide enough to fit a 4 foot tall child inside

a shrimp's heart is in its head

all polar bears are left handed.

approximately 70 percent of the earth is covered by water. only 1 percent of this water is drinkable

babies are born without knee caps.

bananas are not fruit! they are a type of herb

coca-cola was the first drink to be consumed in outer space

sound travels 15 times faster through steel than through air

the average iceberg weighs 20,000 tons

the longest word in the english language is pneumonoultramicroscopicsilicovolcanoconioses

you share your birthday with at least 9 million other people in the world

cold water weighs more than hot water

month

day 15:

written by i like ...

written by i like ...

day 16:

i like ...

i like ...

day 17:

i like ...

i like ...

day 18:

i like ...

i like ...

day 19:

i like ...

i like ...

day 20:

i like ...

i like ...

day 21:

i like ...

i like ...

your turn

month

day 22:

written by — i like ...

written by — i like ...

day 23:

i like ...

i like ...

day 24:

i like ...

i like ...

day 25:

i like ...

i like ...

day 26:

i like ...

i like ...

day 27:

i like ...

i like ...

day 28:

i like ...

i like ...

i like...holding your hand.

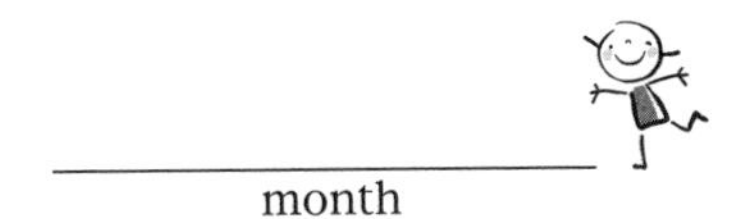

month

day 29:

written by i like ...

written by i like ...

day 30:

i like ...

i like ...

day 31:

i like ...

i like ...

just for kids

what do you **like** about your family, friends, life or **you**?

my name i like ...

i like ...

i like ...

(kids too young to write? feel free to write on their behalf.)

imagine

sing love

run

color play

dance

draw splash

smile like

doodle

giggle

explore laugh

hug paint

smooch

dream

month

day 1:

written by i like ...

written by i like ...

day 2:

i like ...

i like ...

day 3:

i like ...

i like ...

day 4:

i like ...

i like ...

day 5:

i like ...

i like ...

day 6:

i like ...

i like ...

day 7:

i like ...

i like ...

i like...your excitement about life.

"tomorrow we can eat broccoli but today is for ice cream."

—mallory

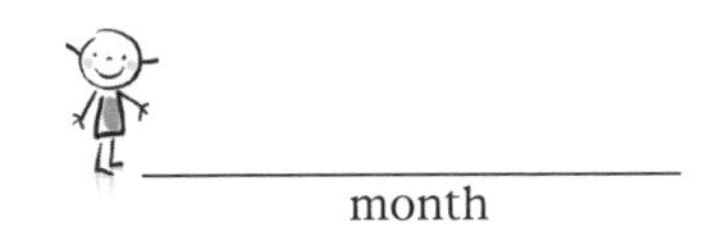

month

day 8:

written by i like ...

written by i like ...

day 9:

i like ...

i like ...

day 10:

i like ...

i like ...

day 11:

i like ...

i like ...

day 12:

i like ...

i like ...

day 13:

i like ...

i like ...

day 14:

i like ...

i like ...

i like...your excitement about life.

trace *your* hand

month

day 15:

written by i like ...

written by i like ...

day 16:

i like ...

i like ...

day 17:

i like ...

i like ...

day 18:

i like ...

i like ...

day 19:

i like ...

i like ...

day 20:

i like ...

i like ...

day 21:

i like ...

i like ...

doodle

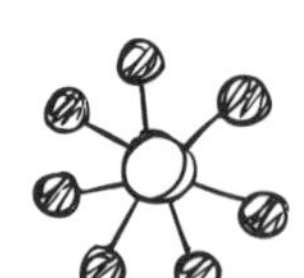

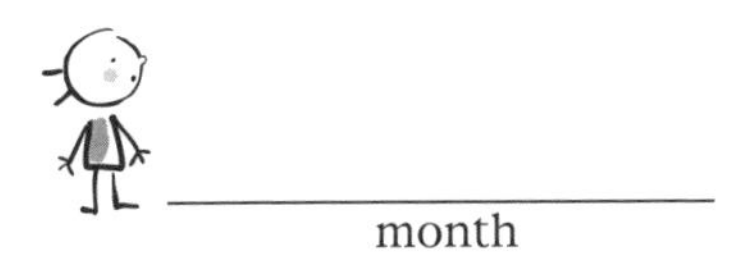

day 22:

written by ______ i like ... ______

______

written by ______ i like ... ______

______

day 23:

______ i like ... ______

______

______ i like ... ______

______

day 24:

______ i like ... ______

______

______ i like ... ______

______

day 25:

______ i like ... ______

______

______ i like ... ______

______

day 26:

______ i like ... ______

______

______ i like ... ______

______

day 27:

______ i like ... ______

______

______ i like ... ______

______

day 28:

______ i like ... ______

______

______ i like ... ______

______

i like...your excitement about life.

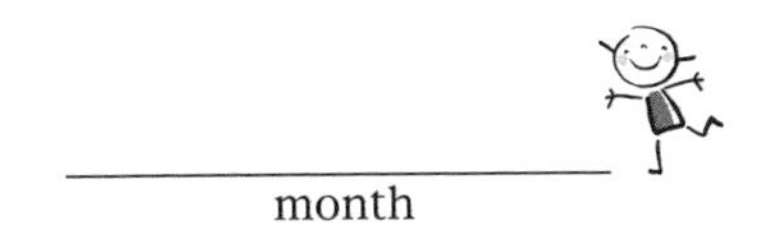

month

day 29:

written by i like ...

written by i like ...

day 30:

i like ...

i like ...

day 31:

i like ...

i like ...

just for kids

what do you **like** about your family, friends, life or **you**?

my name i like ...

i like ...

i like ...

(kids too young to write? feel free to write on their behalf.)

IF YOU
ARE FEELING
BLUE, TRY
PAINTING
YOURSELF
A DIFFERENT
COLOR.
—HANNAH

____
month

day 1:

________ written by i like ... ________________

________ written by i like ... ________________

day 2:

________ i like ... ________________

________ i like ... ________________

day 3:

________ i like ... ________________

________ i like ... ________________

day 4:

________ i like ... ________________

________ i like ... ________________

day 5:

________ i like ... ________________

________ i like ... ________________

day 6:

________ i like ... ________________

________ i like ... ________________

day 7:

________ i like ... ________________

________ i like ... ________________

i like...listening to you giggle.

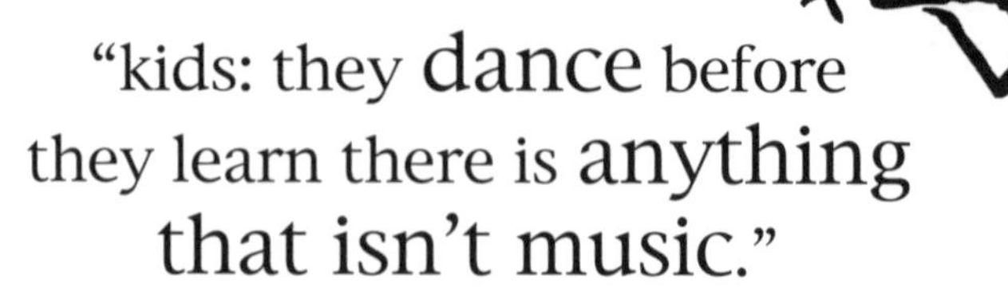

"kids: they dance before they learn there is anything that isn't music."

—william stafford

place your photo here

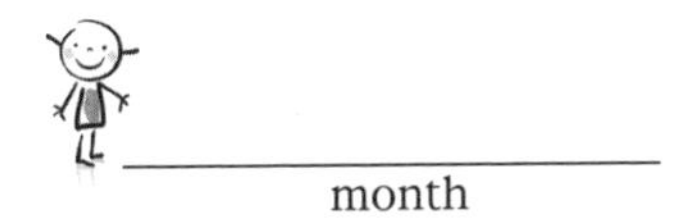

month

day 8:

written by ______ i like ... ______

written by ______ i like ... ______

day 9:

______ i like ... ______

______ i like ... ______

day 10:

______ i like ... ______

______ i like ... ______

day 11:

______ i like ... ______

______ i like ... ______

day 12:

______ i like ... ______

______ i like ... ______

day 13:

______ i like ... ______

______ i like ... ______

day 14:

______ i like ... ______

______ i like ... ______

i like...listening to you giggle.

if i had my child to raise all over again ...

i'd build self esteem first and the house later.

i'd finger paint more and point the finger less.

i would do less correcting and more connecting.

i would take my eyes off my watch and watch
with my eyes.

i'd take more hikes and fly more kites.

i'd stop playing serious and seriously play.

i would run through more fields and gaze
at more stars.

i'd do more hugging and less tugging.

i'd see the oak tree in the acorn more often.

i would be firm less often and affirm much more.

i'd model less about the love of power and more
about the power of love.

—diane loomans

month

day 15:

written by i like ...

written by i like ...

day 16:

i like ...

i like ...

day 17:

i like ...

i like ...

day 18:

i like ...

i like ...

day 19:

i like ...

i like ...

day 20:

i like ...

i like ...

day 21:

i like ...

i like ...

i like...listening to you giggle.

i like ...

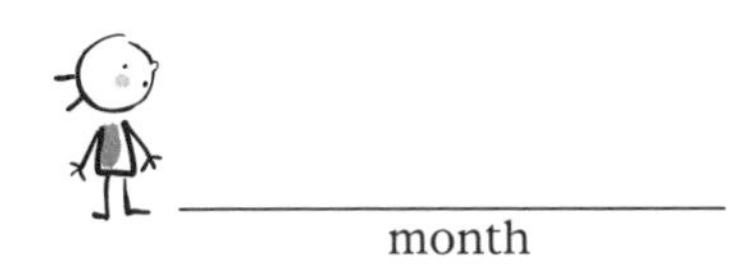

month

day 22:

written by ______ i like ... ______

written by ______ i like ... ______

day 23:

______ i like ... ______

______ i like ... ______

day 24:

______ i like ... ______

______ i like ... ______

day 25:

______ i like ... ______

______ i like ... ______

day 26:

______ i like ... ______

______ i like ... ______

day 27:

______ i like ... ______

______ i like ... ______

day 28:

______ i like ... ______

______ i like ... ______

i like...listening to you giggle.

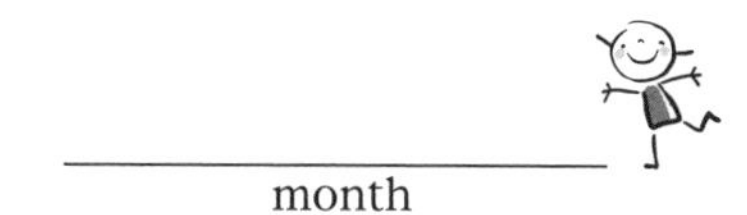

month

day 29:

written by i like ...

written by i like ...

day 30:

i like ...

i like ...

day 31:

i like ...

i like ...

just for kids

what do you like about your family, friends, life or you?

my name i like ...

i like ...

i like ...

(kids too young to write? feel free to write on their behalf.)

_______________ 
month

day 1:

_______________ written by i like ... _______________

____

_______________ written by i like ... _______________

____

day 2:

_______________ i like ... _______________

____

_______________ i like ... _______________

____

day 3:

_______________ i like ... _______________

____

_______________ i like ... _______________

____

day 4:

_______________ i like ... _______________

____

_______________ i like ... _______________

____

day 5:

_______________ i like ... _______________

____

_______________ i like ... _______________

____

day 6:

_______________ i like ... _______________

____

_______________ i like ... _______________

____

day 7:

_______________ i like ... _______________

____

_______________ i like ... _______________

____

i like...when you are happy.

place your photo here
place your photo here
place your photo here
you are a superstar

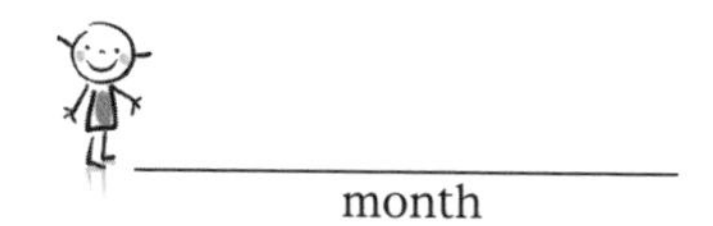

day 8:

written by ______ i like ... ______

______

written by ______ i like ... ______

______

day 9:

______ i like ... ______

______

______ i like ... ______

______

day 10:

______ i like ... ______

______

______ i like ... ______

______

day 11:

______ i like ... ______

______

______ i like ... ______

______

day 12:

______ i like ... ______

______

______ i like ... ______

______

day 13:

______ i like ... ______

______

______ i like ... ______

______

day 14:

______ i like ... ______

______

______ i like ... ______

______

i like...when you are happy.

for Kids

Like Book

chang Lives one Heart at a time

caution: This book may cause fantastic relationships

Love,
Naomi

month

day 15:

written by ________ i like ... ________

written by ________ i like ... ________

day 16:

________ i like ... ________

________ i like ... ________

day 17:

________ i like ... ________

________ i like ... ________

day 18:

________ i like ... ________

________ i like ... ________

day 19:

________ i like ... ________

________ i like ... ________

day 20:

________ i like ... ________

________ i like ... ________

day 21:

________ i like ... ________

________ i like ... ________

jot it down

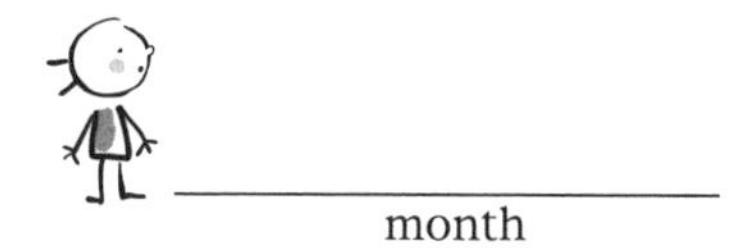

month

day 22:

written by i like ...

written by i like ...

day 23:

i like ...

i like ...

day 24:

i like ...

i like ...

day 25:

i like ...

i like ...

day 26:

i like ...

i like ...

day 27:

i like ...

i like ...

day 28:

i like ...

i like ...

i like...when you are happy.

month

day 29:

written by i like ...

written by i like ...

day 30:

i like ...

i like ...

day 31:

i like ...

i like ...

just for kids

what do you **like** about your family, friends, life or **you**?

my name i like ...

i like ...

i like ...

(kids too young to write? feel free to write on their behalf.)

be happy

be true be silly

be real

be loved

be

be nice be free

be gentle

be wild be kind

be you

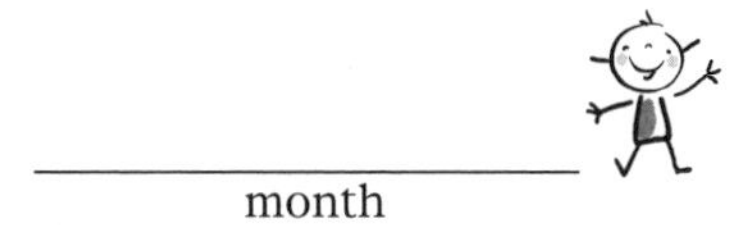

month

day 1:

written by ______ i like ... ______

written by ______ i like ... ______

day 2:

______ i like ... ______

______ i like ... ______

day 3:

______ i like ... ______

______ i like ... ______

day 4:

______ i like ... ______

______ i like ... ______

day 5:

______ i like ... ______

______ i like ... ______

day 6:

______ i like ... ______

______ i like ... ______

day 7:

______ i like ... ______

______ i like ... ______

i like...that you see magic in the small stuff.

"count your rainbows not your thunderstorms."

—alyssa

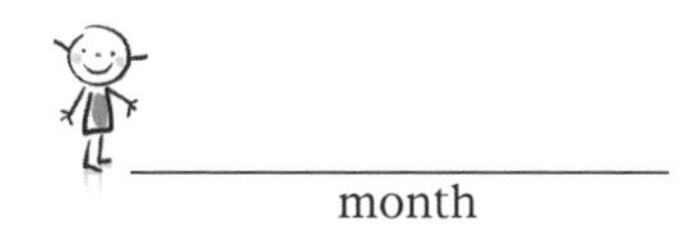

month

day 8:

written by ______ i like ... ______

written by ______ i like ... ______

day 9:

______ i like ... ______

______ i like ... ______

day 10:

______ i like ... ______

______ i like ... ______

day 11:

______ i like ... ______

______ i like ... ______

day 12:

______ i like ... ______

______ i like ... ______

day 13:

______ i like ... ______

______ i like ... ______

day 14:

______ i like ... ______

______ i like ... ______

i like...that you see magic in the small stuff.

the eyes of love

a grandmother and a little girl whose face was sprinkled with bright red freckles spent the day at the zoo. the children were waiting in line to get their cheeks painted by a local artist who was decorating them with tiger paws.

'you've got so many freckles, there's no place to paint!' a boy in the line cried.

embarrassed, the little girl dropped her head. Her grandmother knelt down next to her. 'i love your freckles,' she said.

'not me,' the girl replied.

'well, when I was a little girl I always wanted freckles,' she said, tracing her finger across the child's cheek. 'freckles are beautiful!'

the girl looked up. 'really?'

'of course,' said the grandmother. 'why, just name me one thing that's prettier than freckles.'

the little girl peered into the old woman's smiling face. 'wrinkles,' she answered softly.

—author unknown

month

day 15:

written by i like ...

written by i like ...

day 16:

i like ...

i like ...

day 17:

i like ...

i like ...

day 18:

i like ...

i like ...

day 19:

i like ...

i like ...

day 20:

i like ...

i like ...

day 21:

i like ...

i like ...

i like...that you see magic in the small stuff.

scribble

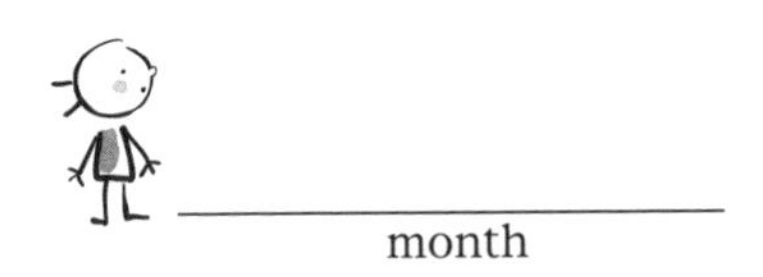

month

day 22:

written by i like ...

written by i like ...

day 23:

i like ...

i like ...

day 24:

i like ...

i like ...

day 25:

i like ...

i like ...

day 26:

i like ...

i like ...

day 27:

i like ...

i like ...

day 28:

i like ...

i like ...

i like...that you see magic in the small stuff.

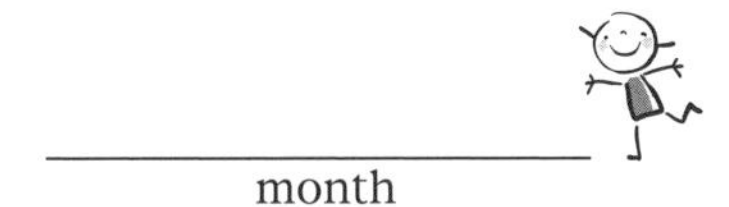

day 29:

written by ____________ i like ... ____________

written by ____________ i like ... ____________

day 30:

____________ i like ... ____________

____________ i like ... ____________

day 31:

____________ i like ... ____________

____________ i like ... ____________

just for kids

what do you like about your family, friends, life or you?

my name ____________ i like ... ____________

____________ i like ... ____________

____________ i like ... ____________

(kids too young to write? feel free to write on their behalf.)

laugh together

take a family
portrait under
the table

2

have a themed
skit night
☆ movies
☆ cartoon characters
☆ make a song
into a skit

reenact something
you would do
everyday in reverse

month

day 1:

written by i like ...

written by i like ...

day 2:

i like ...

i like ...

day 3:

i like ...

i like ...

day 4:

i like ...

i like ...

day 5:

i like ...

i like ...

day 6:

i like ...

i like ...

day 7:

i like ...

i like ...

i like...your innocence.

"the only thing worth stealing is a kiss from a sleeping baby."

—joe houldsworth

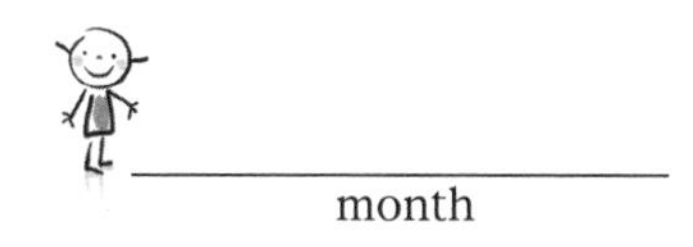

month

day 8:
written by i like ...

written by i like ...

day 9:
i like ...

i like ...

day 10:
i like ...

i like ...

day 11:
i like ...

i like ...

day 12:
i like ...

i like ...

day 13:
i like ...

i like ...

day 14:
i like ...

i like ...

i like...your innocence.

how do you talk to yourself?

a man and his small son were out walking through the mountains and at one point, the little boy slipped 20-30 yards down the mountain side. finally he was able to grab onto a tree branch and hold on, then he screamed out, "help me!"

this voice boomed back, "help me!"

he looked kind of confused and yelled, "who are you?"

the voice boomed back, "who are you?"

the small boy was aggravated and said, "you are a fool!"

the voice came back, "you are a fool!"

he said, "you are a coward!"

the voice yelled back, "you are a coward!"

just about that time, his father got to him. the small boy asked his dad, "who is that?"

his dad laughed and said, "son, that's called an echo but really its called life. see, let me show you something son."

the dad hollered out, "you are a winner!"

the voice boomed back, "you are a winner!"

"you are talented!"

it came back, "you are talented!"

the dad yelled, "you've got what it takes!"

the voice rang out, "you've got what it takes!"

the dad said, "son, that's how life is. whatever you send out always comes back to you. the question is, what are you sending out about yourself? start sending out i am strong, i am talented, and i am the best. i'll make it, i am creative, i am healthy, i am prosperous and i am victorious. what you send out is going to come back to you. don't dare go through life being against yourself."

—unknown author

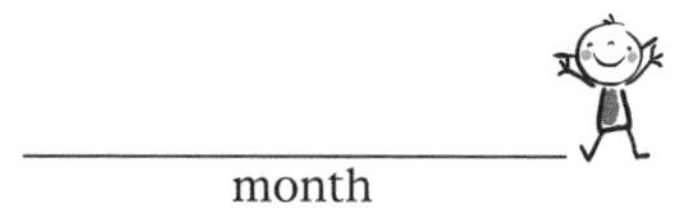

month

day 15:

written by i like ...

written by i like ...

day 16:

i like ...

i like ...

day 17:

i like ...

i like ...

day 18:

i like ...

i like ...

day 19:

i like ...

i like ...

day 20:

i like ...

i like ...

day 21:

i like ...

i like ...

i like...your innocence.

shout it out

month

day 22:

written by i like ...

written by i like ...

day 23:

i like ...

i like ...

day 24:

i like ...

i like ...

day 25:

i like ...

i like ...

day 26:

i like ...

i like ...

day 27:

i like ...

i like ...

day 28:

i like ...

i like ...

i like...your innocence.

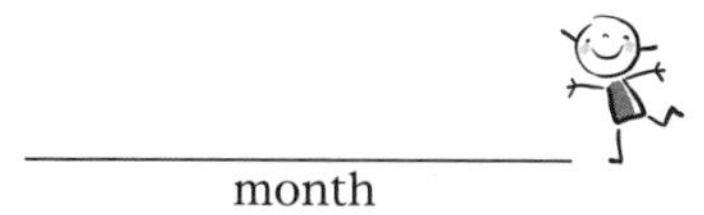

day 29:

written by ______ i like ... ______

______

written by ______ i like ... ______

______

day 30:

______ i like ... ______

______

______ i like ... ______

______

day 31:

______ i like ... ______

______

______ i like ... ______

______

just for kids

what do you like about your family, friends, life or you?

my name ______ i like ... ______

______

______

______ i like ... ______

______

______

______ i like ... ______

______

______

(kids too young to write? feel free to write on their behalf.)

"to the world you may be one person
but to one person you may
be the world."

—author unknown

month

day 1:

written by i like ...

written by i like ...

day 2:

i like ...

i like ...

day 3:

i like ...

i like ...

day 4:

i like ...

i like ...

day 5:

i like ...

i like ...

day 6:

i like ...

i like ...

day 7:

i like ...

i like ...

i like...how peaceful you look when you sleep.

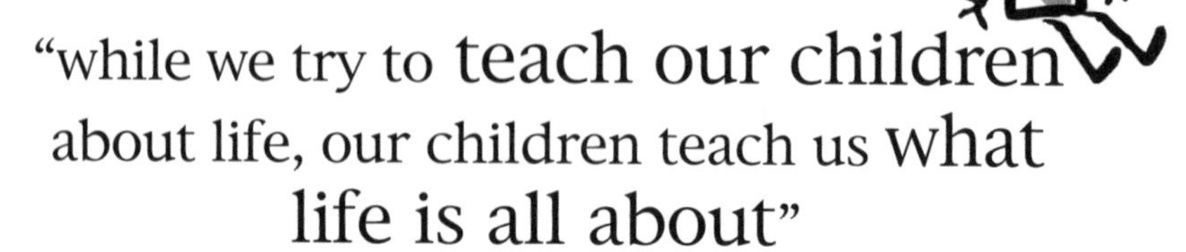

"while we try to teach our children about life, our children teach us what life is all about"

—angela schwindt

place your photo here

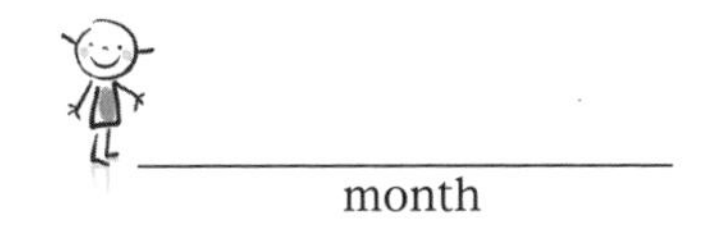

day 8:

written by ______ i like ... ______

______

written by ______ i like ... ______

______

day 9:

______ i like ... ______

______

______ i like ... ______

______

day 10:

______ i like ... ______

______

______ i like ... ______

______

day 11:

______ i like ... ______

______

______ i like ... ______

______

day 12:

______ i like ... ______

______

______ i like ... ______

______

day 13:

______ i like ... ______

______

______ i like ... ______

______

day 14:

______ i like ... ______

______

______ i like ... ______

______

i like...how peaceful you look when you sleep.

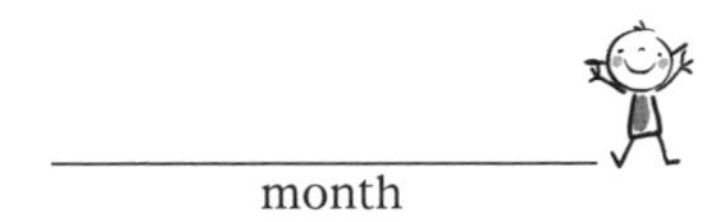

day 15:

written by ____________ i like ... ____________

____

written by ____________ i like ... ____________

____

day 16:

____________ i like ... ____________

____

____________ i like ... ____________

____

day 17:

____________ i like ... ____________

____

____________ i like ... ____________

____

day 18:

____________ i like ... ____________

____

____________ i like ... ____________

____

day 19:

____________ i like ... ____________

____

____________ i like ... ____________

____

day 20:

____________ i like ... ____________

____

____________ i like ... ____________

____

day 21:

____________ i like ... ____________

____

____________ i like ... ____________

____

i like...how **peaceful you look** when you sleep.

think out loud

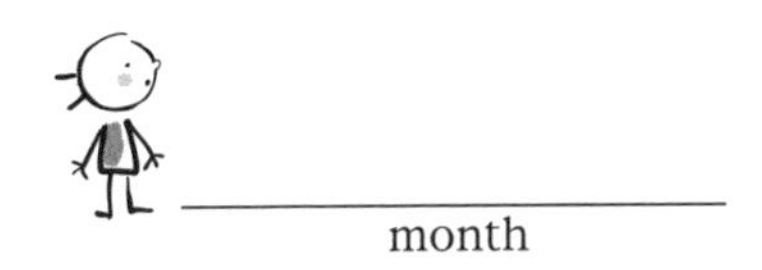

day 22:

written by ________ i like ... ________

____

written by ________ i like ... ________

____

day 23:

________ i like ... ________

____

________ i like ... ________

____

day 24:

________ i like ... ________

____

________ i like ... ________

____

day 25:

________ i like ... ________

____

________ i like ... ________

____

day 26:

________ i like ... ________

____

________ i like ... ________

____

day 27:

________ i like ... ________

____

________ i like ... ________

____

day 28:

________ i like ... ________

____

________ i like ... ________

____

i like...how peaceful you look when you sleep.

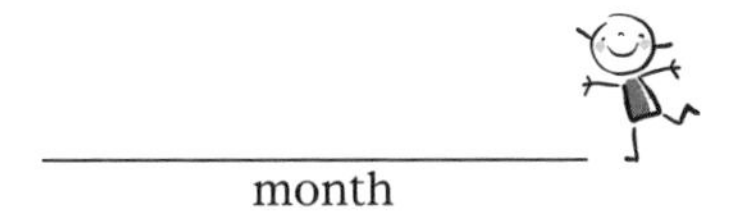

month

day 29:

written by i like ...

written by i like ...

day 30:

i like ...

i like ...

day 31:

i like ...

i like ...

just for kids

what do you like about your family, friends, life or you?

my name i like ...

i like ...

i like ...

(kids too young to write? feel free to write on their behalf.)

i like ...

...you

month

day 1:

written by — i like ...

written by — i like ...

day 2:

i like ...

i like ...

day 3:

i like ...

i like ...

day 4:

i like ...

i like ...

day 5:

i like ...

i like ...

day 6:

i like ...

i like ...

day 7:

i like ...

i like ...

i like...your hugs.

what is love according to children?

when someone loves you, the way they say your name is different. you just know that your name is safe in their mouths. — billy

love is when you go out to eat and give somebody most of your french fries without making them give you any of theirs. — chrissy

love is what makes you smile when you're tired. — terri

love is when my mommy makes coffee for my daddy and she takes a sip giving it to him, to make sure the taste is ok. — danny

love is chocolate chip cookie bars at grandma's house. — jackson

love is when you tell a guy you like his shirt, then he wears it everyday. — noelle

love is like a little old woman and a little old man who are still friends, even after they know each other so well. — tommy

my mommy loves me more than anybody. you don't see anyone else kissing me to sleep at night. — clare

love is when your puppy licks your face even after you left him alone all day. — mary ann

love is when mommy gives me a hug and a kiss and a pat pat pat. — austin

when you love somebody, your eyelashes go up and down and little stars come out of you. — karen

when my grandma got arthritis, she couldn't bend over and paint her toenails anymore. so my grandpa does it for her now all the time, even when his hands got arthritis too. that's love. — rebecca

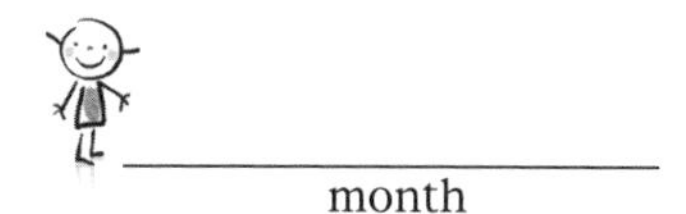

month

day 8:

written by i like ...

written by i like ...

day 9:

i like ...

i like ...

day 10:

i like ...

i like ...

day 11:

i like ...

i like ...

day 12:

i like ...

i like ...

day 13:

i like ...

i like ...

day 14:

i like ...

i like ...

i like...your hugs.

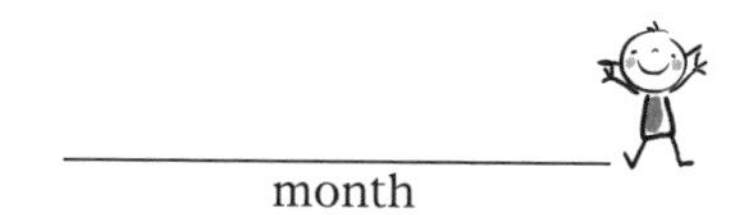

day 15:

written by ______ i like ... ______

written by ______ i like ... ______

day 16:

______ i like ... ______

______ i like ... ______

day 17:

______ i like ... ______

______ i like ... ______

day 18:

______ i like ... ______

______ i like ... ______

day 19:

______ i like ... ______

______ i like ... ______

day 20:

______ i like ... ______

______ i like ... ______

day 21:

______ i like ... ______

______ i like ... ______

i like...your hugs.

freestyle

month

day 22:

written by i like ...

written by i like ...

day 23:

i like ...

i like ...

day 24:

i like ...

i like ...

day 25:

i like ...

i like ...

day 26:

i like ...

i like ...

day 27:

i like ...

i like ...

day 28:

i like ...

i like ...

i like...your hugs.

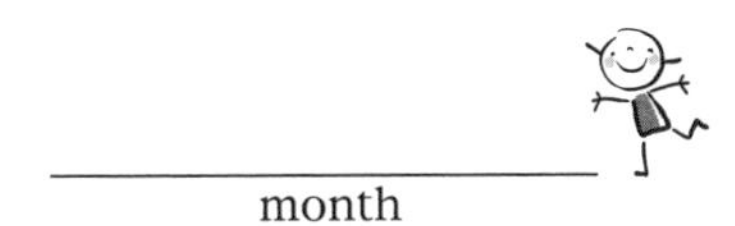

month

day 29:

written by i like ...

written by i like ...

day 30:

i like ...

i like ...

day 31:

i like ...

i like ...

just for kids

what do you like about your family, friends, life or you?

my name i like ...

i like ...

i like ...

(kids too young to write? feel free to write on their behalf.)

"there are no seven wonders of
the world in the eyes of a child.
there are seven million."

—walt streightiff

month

day 1:

written by i like ...

written by i like ...

day 2:

i like ...

i like ...

day 3:

i like ...

i like ...

day 4:

i like ...

i like ...

day 5:

i like ...

i like ...

day 6:

i like ...

i like ...

day 7:

i like ...

i like ...

place your photo here

month

day 8:

written by i like ...

written by i like ...

day 9:

i like ...

i like ...

day 10:

i like ...

i like ...

day 11:

i like ...

i like ...

day 12:

i like ...

i like ...

day 13:

i like ...

i like ...

day 14:

i like ...

i like ...

"a child can ask questions
that a wiseman cannot answer."

—unknown author

month

day 15:

written by i like ...

written by i like ...

day 16:

i like ...

i like ...

day 17:

i like ...

i like ...

day 18:

i like ...

i like ...

day 19:

i like ...

i like ...

day 20:

i like ...

i like ...

day 21:

i like ...

i like ...

create

month

day 22:

written by i like ...

written by i like ...

day 23:

i like ...

i like ...

day 24:

i like ...

i like ...

day 25:

i like ...

i like ...

day 26:

i like ...

i like ...

day 27:

i like ...

i like ...

day 28:

i like ...

i like ...

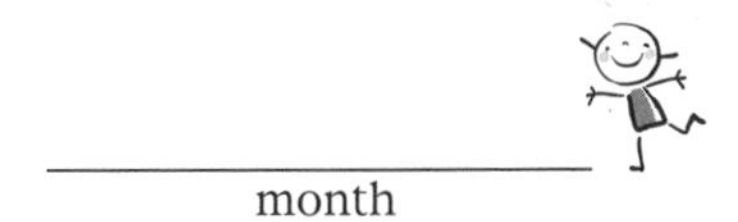

month

day 29:

written by ________ i like ... ________

____

written by ________ i like ... ________

____

day 30:

________ i like ... ________

____

________ i like ... ________

____

day 31:

________ i like ... ________

____

________ i like ... ________

____

just for kids

what do you **like** about your family, friends, life or **you**?

my name ________ i like ... ________

____

____

________ i like ... ________

____

____

________ i like ... ________

____

____

(kids too young to write? feel free to write on their behalf.)

notes & thoughts

notes & thoughts

notes & thoughts

notes & thoughts

CONGRATULATIONS!

you have completed your

the world is a better place
because you are in it!

great gifts for everyone and any occasion!

send books to:

____
name/company

____
street address

____
city state zip

e-mail ____

contact phone (____)______________________________

i like book for couples, please indicate number of copies ____

i like book for kids, please indicate number of copies for:
blue (____) pink (____) purple (____) green (____)
orange (____) red (____)

please visit www.theilikebook.com for pricing.

payment method:

________ check/money order
(please make checks payable to: Lucky Looney LLC)

please send order form with check/money order to:
the i like book
p.o. box 4091
parker, co. 80134

all credit card and paypal orders can be made at www.theilikebook.com

comments____
____
____

contact: the i like book—p.o. box 4091, parker co 80134
tel: (888)737-like www.theilikebook.com

titles to pick up now

"the i like book for couples"
meredith & lance j. looney

a like book for couples? yes, we know what you're thinking; my partner already knows what i like about them. but do they really know? do you know what your partner likes about you? the i like book brings fun & depth into any relationship. when you focus on the simple likes about your partner, you might begin to really like your relationship more than you ever thought possible.

"the five love languages of children"
dr. gary chapman & dr. ross campbell

primary love languages begin to take shape at an early age in children—but the need to feel loved begins and grows right away. with dr. ross campbell's expertise in child development, dr. gary chapman applies his love languages concept to children. learn to strengthen the bond you and your children share by speaking their language.

"positive personality profiles"
robert a. rohm

this book gives a basic overview preferences for each style. this book provides a foundation for understanding the DISC approach to human behavior. It is written to edify people and give clear understanding on gifts, talents and effectiveness of behavioral styles.

about us

as authors, entrepreneurs and parents of two active boys, lance & meredith looney have helped strengthen the lives of children, parents and couples through their ground-breaking daily books, **the i like book** for kids and **the i like book** for couples. after spending many years in corporate america, lance & meredith, set out on a journey to help people create "fantastic relationships" by promoting a back-to-the-basics philosophy of positive attention and moments of meaningful reflection with loved ones. you can visit their website at www.theilikebook.com

what people are saying about the i like book

"the i like book has shown me a new way of life. i now realize the many things i like about my children and grandchildren as well as how much i love them. the i like book is making a positive impact in the world."

—karen, mother of three & grandmother of four

"there will never be a better investment of your time than of the few short moments each day that you incorporate this book into your child's life. when you utilize the i like book, something more special than you ever dreamed will be created."

—travis, father of two

"this is a simple, yet wonderful, tool for any parent."

—louise, mother of one & grandmother of two

"this amazing book has reinvented relationships between the teachers and kids at lightway at sloans childcare! actively looking for positive likes within each child has been priceless."

—klare, mother of two, childcare & preschool owner

"we have four children in our busy home. the i like book is a blessing because it allows each child to feel uniquely special."

—tammi, mother of four

www.theilikebook.com